nature challenge

DO IT! SCORE IT!

Published by Collins
An imprint of HarperCollins Publishers
Westerhill Road, Bishopbriggs, Glasgow G64 2QT
www.harpercollins.co.uk

HarperCollins Publishers
1st Floor, Watermarque Building, Ringsend Road, Dublin 4, Ireland

A catalogue record for this book is available from the British Library.

ISBN 9780008529772

Printed in Bosnia and Herzegovina

10 9 8 7 6 5 4 3 2 1

Text by Heather Ryce
Front cover image © Coatesy/Shutterstock.com
All internal images © Shutterstock.com except p8 (below) © Tetra Images, LLC / Alamy Stock Photo, p10 © Richard Kellett / Alamy Stock Photo, and pages 12-13, 22-25, 42, 52, 76 (below), 78 and 88 courtesy of Jennifer Smith and Oliver Smith.

MIX
Paper from responsible sources
FSC™ C007454

This book is produced from independently certified FSC™ paper to ensure responsible forest management.

For more information visit: www.harpercollins.co.uk/green

nature challenge

DO IT! SCORE IT!

Contents

Tick off each activity as you do it!

How to use this book

Get ready to take on the i-SPY challenge with 50 activities to get closer to nature!

Once you've done each activity tick it off on the contents list. You can do them in any order you like.

Note to grown-up: Join in the fun by doing the activities together and supervise any that you feel necessary.

Look out for activities which have eco points. These are awarded for doing something that helps look after the planet and its wildlife. Once you score 200 eco points, send off for your i-SPY eco-hero certificate and badge.

As well as activities, the book is packed with facts, photos and things to spot. If you spy it, score it by ticking the circle or star. Items with a star are difficult to spot so you'll have to search high and low to find them. Once you score 1000 spotter points, send off for your i-SPY super-spotter certificate and badge.

How to get your i-SPY certificates and badges

✔ Ask a grown-up to check your score.

✔ Apply for your certificate and badge at collins.co.uk/i-SPY (if you are under the age of 13 you'll need a parent or guardian to do this).

✔ We'll send you your certificate and badge!

Keep a nature diary

Record every detail of your wild adventures.

You'll need:

notepad/diary, pen, pencil, glue or eco tape (if you want to stick things in your diary)

What to do:

1. Make a note of the date of your diary entry and what the weather was like on that day.
2. Write about where you were and how it made you feel.
3. What did you see, hear, smell, taste and touch?
4. What was something new you learned about nature?
5. Draw a picture to describe your day – the more colourful the better.

Score 10 eco points if you decorate your diary with natural things like leaves and dried flowers rather than man-made materials like glitter and stickers.

10 ECO POINTS

Go on a nature walk

Going outside and walking in nature can help fill you with happy thoughts and gives you lots of energy. It's always exciting as you never know what you may spot!

Choose somewhere to go for a walk. It could be anywhere, for example your local park or nearby woods. Then, use ALL your senses to take in what's around you. What can you see, smell, hear, taste and feel? Find something...

Climb a hill...

Hillwalking is a fun hobby and the biggest hills, or mountains, in the UK are found mostly in Scotland and Wales. A hill in Scotland that is over 914 metres (3000 feet) is called a Munro – that's the height of three Eiffel Towers stacked on top of one another!

You'll need:

walking shoes, warm clothes, bottle of water, snacks

What to do:

You don't need to climb Ben Nevis to do some hillwalking! Why not find a hill near to where you live, climb to the top and enjoy the view? Remember to bring along your nature diary and write down everything you see from the peak.

...and roll back down

If the hill you have climbed isn't too high and it is safe to do so (always check with a grown-up first), why not roll down to the bottom? If you need to stop mid-roll just throw your arms and legs out like a starfish!

Here are some things you might spot while you're out hillwalking.

Cairn

Cairns are usually small piles of rocks that mark a path on a hill. They're helpful for navigating if it's foggy.

5 POINTS

Trig point

A concrete pillar that marks the summit of a hill or mountain.

10 POINTS

Rock climber

Look to see if they've got a jazzy chalk bag!

15 POINTS

Geocache

A GPS treasure hunt – check out **geocache.com** for how to take part.

25 POINTS

Make a nature wheel

The year is divided up into four seasons: spring, summer, autumn and winter – each lasting three months. The different seasons impact nature in many ways, with lots of birds being born in spring, leaves falling from the trees in autumn and animals hibernating through the cold of winter.

By keeping a nature wheel, you will clearly see how the weather differs across the seasons and how the colour of the sky changes for example.

You'll need:

paper plate,
ruler, marker,
coloured pencils
or crayons

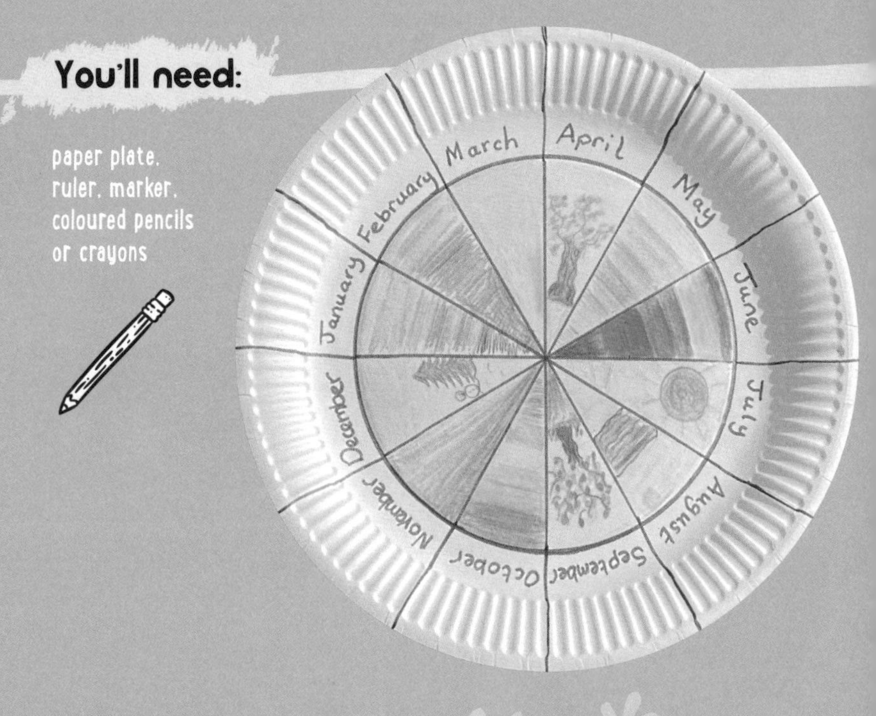

What to do:

1. Use your marker to draw around the inner circle of the plate.

2. Then, with your marker and ruler, divide your plate into four equal sections by drawing a line horizontally down the centre and a vertical line across the plate.

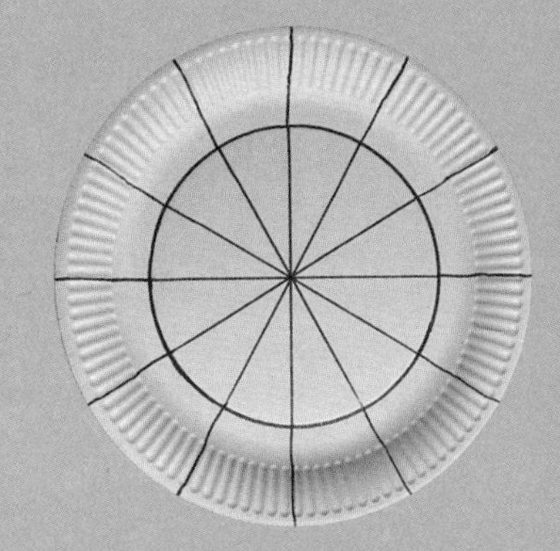

3. Then divide each section into three equal sized triangles (you can do this by drawing two diagonal lines from the outside of your plate to the centre point).

4. Repeat this in each section so you finish with twelve triangles drawn on to your plate.

5. Label each triangle with a month of the year, use the blank space between the inner circle you drew and the edge of the plate – start with your birthday month and work clockwise around!

6. As a month passes fill in the appropriate triangle with colours or a drawing which reminds you of that month. For instance, September could be full of oranges and browns as it may remind you of all the leaves falling off the trees. June could have a large sun drawn in as it reminds you of the warm summer.

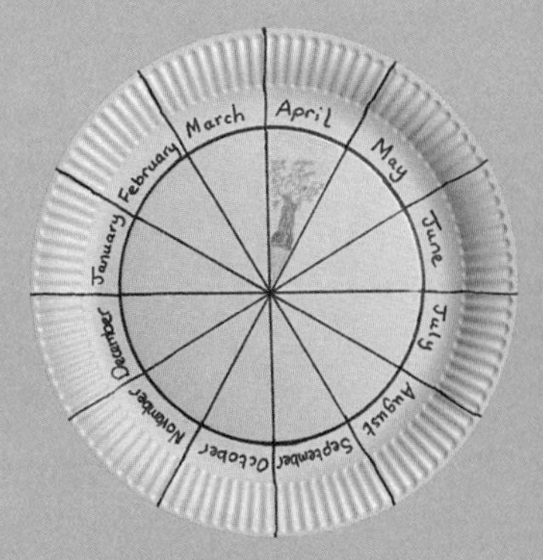

7. At the end of the year hang your plate up and look back at all the changes that have occurred throughout the seasons!

5

Watch a murmuration of starlings

Starlings are social birds and prefer to feed and roost in large groups. In the winter evenings, as the Sun is setting, they will gather (sometimes into the thousands) in the sky. This large group of flying birds is known as a 'murmuration'. A murmuration forms incredible shapes and patterns as the birds dance and swirl around one another. At the end of the performance, they will dive back towards the ground to their roost spot where they will spend the night. It's something everyone must see at least once!

You'll need:

warm clothes, binoculars (not essential)

What to do:

1. Ask an adult to find, or find for out yourself, an area where murmurations take place. This can be in the countryside, open fields and even in towns and cities.

2. Arrive half an hour before the Sun goes down and find a place with a clear view of the sky.

3. Be patient and you may just see the spectacular, ever-changing shapes of a starling murmuration!

Starlings aren't the only types of birds that gather in groups. Check out these fun collective nouns for different groups of birds, and see if you can spot any for yourself...

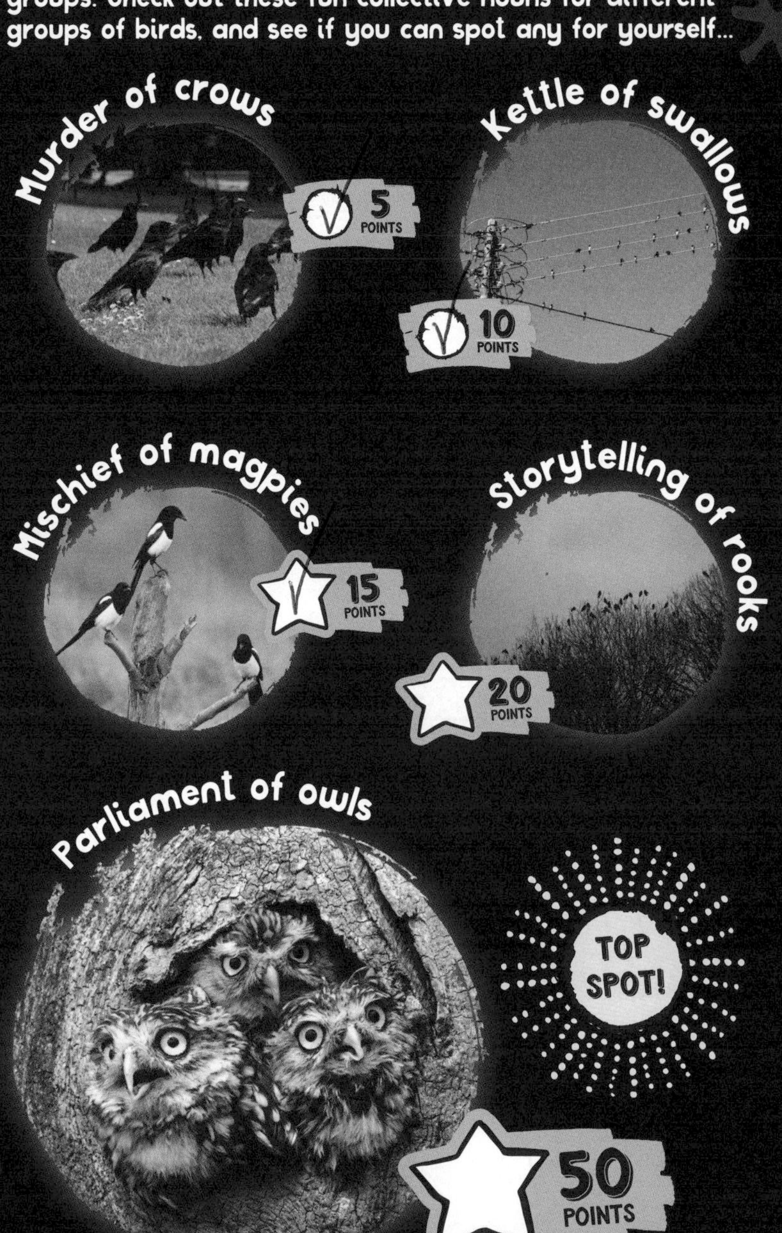

Identify bird feathers

Birds are unique as they are the only group of animals with feathers. The number of feathers they have depends on the type of bird – songbirds have up to 3000 covering their bodies, birds of prey up to 8000 and swans can have up to 25,000 feathers!

Feathers are made from keratin, which is the same protein as human hair, and like our hair, feathers help keep birds warm. Also, just like the hair on our head, birds' feathers fall out as new ones grow through.

Go into your garden or a nearby park and see if you can find any fallen feathers. Then, try to identify which bird they came from. Score points if you find any of the feathers below.

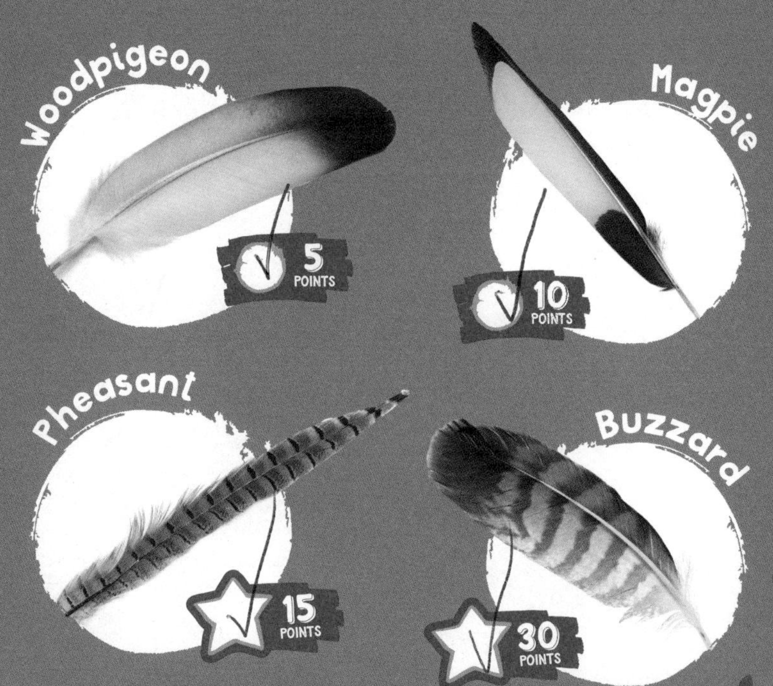

Make a quill pen from a feather

Once you've identified any feathers you've collected, it's time to put them to good use.

You'll need:

feather, basin, scissors, toothpick, food colouring

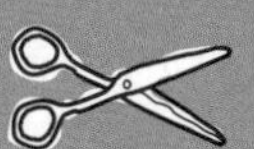

What to do:

1. Clean the bird's feather in a basin of warm water.
2. Ask a grown-up to help make a diagonal cut in the shaft of the feather using the scissors, so that the quill ends in a point just like a pen.
3. Use the toothpick to remove any dirt from inside the hollow shaft.
4. To make ink, mix two tablespoons of water with around 10 drops of food colouring.
5. Dip your new quill pen into the ink you've made and start writing.

8

Spot nature colours

Colour in nature is important. Lots of flowers have brightly coloured petals to attract bees and many birds have colourful feathers to show off how healthy they are. Some insects and animals use colour to let others know they are dangerous and should be left alone.

We know that the grass is green, and the sky is blue, but how many other colours can you see when you go for a walk or cycle outside? Can you spot something...

There is one thing in nature that includes lots of colours... a rainbow.

Rainbow

Rainbows are formed when light shines through water. So when sunlight shines through rain, you see a rainbow. You might also see a rainbow if you're using a hosepipe, for example. If the sunlight shines through your jet of water, it might create a mini rainbow!

Double rainbow

If you see two rainbows side-by-side, this is a rare treat!

30
POINTS

Snowbow

Snowbows are very rare, especially in the UK, but happen when sunlight shines through snowflakes in the air.

50
POINTS

TOP SPOT!

9

Watch clouds

Have you noticed there are different types of clouds in the sky? Clouds can give you an idea of what the weather will be – whether you may need your sunglasses or if it is best to take an umbrella with you if you'll be going outside!

When warm air rises and begins to cool, the cooler air can't hold as much water vapour, and it starts to condense (changes from a gas to a liquid). This causes lots of water droplets to form resulting in the droplets in the sky becoming the clouds we see.

What to do:

1. Spend some time outside cloud watching! Ask an adult to take you somewhere you can look for clouds – it could be your garden, a park or a school field.

2. Pick a safe, quiet spot on the ground (you could even bring a blanket to lie on for extra comfort), lie back and have a look at the clouds above.

3. What shapes and patterns can you spot high up in the sky? Make a note of what the clouds look like and see if you can identify them from the types of clouds on the opposite page.

Cumulus

These are fluffy, cauliflower-shaped clouds that tend to be brilliant white as they reflect light from the Sun. Their appearance suggests fair weather, often popping up on sunny days.

Cirrus

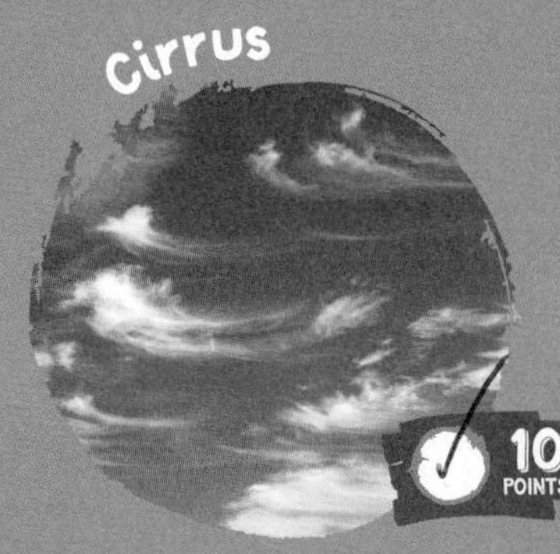

These are stretched, wispy-looking clouds which are made up of ice crystals rather than water droplets. They tend to be associated with good weather.

Nimbus

These are dark grey, shapeless layers of cloud that tend to be thick enough to block out the Sun. They indicate stormy conditions with rainfall.

Stratus

These clouds form a thick blanket over the sky and can be a sign that rain is on its way if it has been warm or snow if it has been cold.

Make a weather vane

This piece of equipment can show you which direction the wind is blowing from, which can tell you if there will be good or bad weather. In the northern hemisphere (countries above the Equator) if the wind is blowing from the north, the weather will get colder and if it is blowing from the south, it will get warmer.

You'll need:

paper cup with lid, 2 straws, piece of card, pin, pen, masking tape, scissors, handful of small stones

What to do:

1. Label the top of the lid of the cup with North (N), South (S), East (E) and West (W) in four equally distanced spaces.

2. Pierce the straw into the centre of the lid of the cup and cover the top of the straw with masking tape.

3. Cut out two triangles with your card, with one triangle slightly larger.

4. Cut two small slits on either side of the second straw and insert the small triangle to one side to make an arrowhead. Then do the same on the other side with the larger triangle but face it in the same direction as the smaller triangle.

5. When your triangles are attached, balance the straw on your finger and find its centre of gravity. Stick a pin through the point where your finger is holding.

6. Pierce the pin through the masking tape end of the first straw so one straw sits on top of the other.

7. Make sure the top straw spins freely.

8. Weigh your cup down by adding stones, and then sit it outside with the 'N' side of the cup facing a north direction.

The way your arrow is pointing will show you which direction the wind is blowing from.

Make a rain gauge

This tool measures how much rain has fallen over a certain period.

You'll need:

2-litre plastic bottle, ruler, scissors, permanent marker, small stones, sellotape

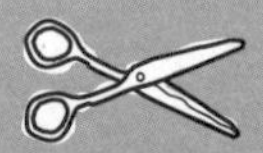

Score 10 eco points for using a recycled plastic bottle to make your rain gauge!

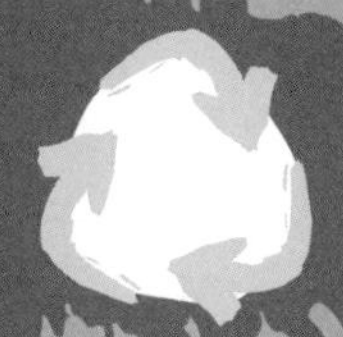

10 ECO POINTS

What to do:

1. Remove the cap and cut the top off the bottle, at the start of the widest point.

2. Fill the bottom of the bottle with small stones to act as a weight.

3. Turn the top section upside down and place back into the bottle.

4. Tape the two bottle pieces together to create a funnel.

5. Using a ruler and permanent marker draw measurements up the side of the bottle in centimetres, starting with the lowest measure towards the bottom. Start the measurement from zero at the top of the pebbles.

6. Place the bottle outside on a level area, make a note of the time and wait for the rain.

In your nature diary keep a note of how much rainwater is collected.

Build a den

Build a den outside and create your own secret nature room.

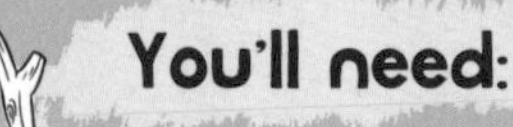

You'll need:

large branches or pieces of wood, an old blanket/rug/sheet, small leafy branches, old cushions/pillows

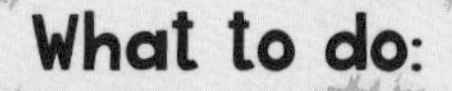

What to do:

1. Use the large branches/pieces of wood to make the frame of your den (remember to leave space for a door). Start by making the walls from the bottom up. Ask a grown-up to help you – this bit can be tricky.
2. Throw your old blanket or sheet over the top to create your roof.
3. Cover your roof with the lighter branches and leaves you have collected to camouflage.
4. Make the inside cosy by adding cushions or pillows to sit on.

Score 10 eco points if your den only uses branches and leaves that have already fallen off trees.

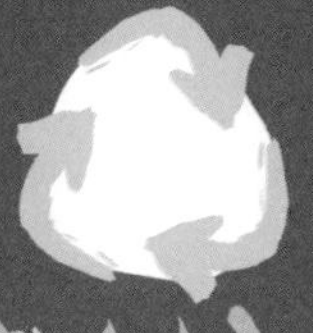

10 ECO POINTS

It's not just humans that might want to make a cosy den or quiet hideaway... animals love to get cosy and shelter from the weather too. While you're out and about, see if you can spot any of these special animal dens.

Mouse hole

5 POINTS

Rabbit warren

10 POINTS

Fox earth

20 POINTS

Badger sett

Camp outdoors and stargaze

Camping outside overnight can be very exciting, but you don't need to go far to have a good time. Camping out in a back garden can be just as much fun and you'll be amazed at how such a familiar place can be so different when the Sun goes down.

You'll need:

sleeping bag, tent, torch, warm clothes, binoculars

What to do:

1. Set up your tent during the day so it is easier to see what you are doing and wait for a clear night so you can make out as many stars as possible. Always make sure a grown-up is camping with you at all times.
2. Planets look very similar to bright stars. One way to tell them apart is if they twinkle or not – stars do, but planets don't. You can see Mercury, Venus, Mars, Jupiter and Saturn from Earth. Shooting stars and satellites will move across the sky.
3. Record every thing you see and even sketch the shape of the Moon on the night you stayed outside.
4. When you've been outside in the dark for a while, your eyes adjust and you can see better in the dark. Torches can spoil that 'night vision'. Making a red filter for your torch can help avoid this though. All you need to do is wrap some red cellophane (like a sweet wrapper) around the end of your torch. Then you can take this book with you and you'll still be able to read it in the dark.

Look out for these features in the night sky.

You might also see the Moon in some of its different phases.

Go on a nocturnal nature walk

You'll need:

warm clothes, torch,
sturdy/comfortable shoes

If you have already gone for a nature walk during the day, go for one in the same location at night, with a grown-up, and notice how many different animals you can see from during the day and all the different noises you can hear.

Walking at night at different times of the year is also a good idea. Nightingale birds visit the UK during summer and in the evening they like to sing loudly from trees! Badger cubs will start to wander from their sett during the spring and you will be able to see animal tracks more easily in the snow during the winter nights.

You could join a local badger watching or bat detecting group to go out in the evening to watch badgers foraging for food near their setts, or record the high-pitched squeaks of bats flying overhead. Other groups record how many toads, frogs and newts they see at night as amphibian numbers are in decline in lots of places. Score 20 eco points if you join a local animal group to help or study nature.

Animals that are active during the night are called nocturnal, and so going on a walk when it is dark gives you a chance to be able to see or hear them.

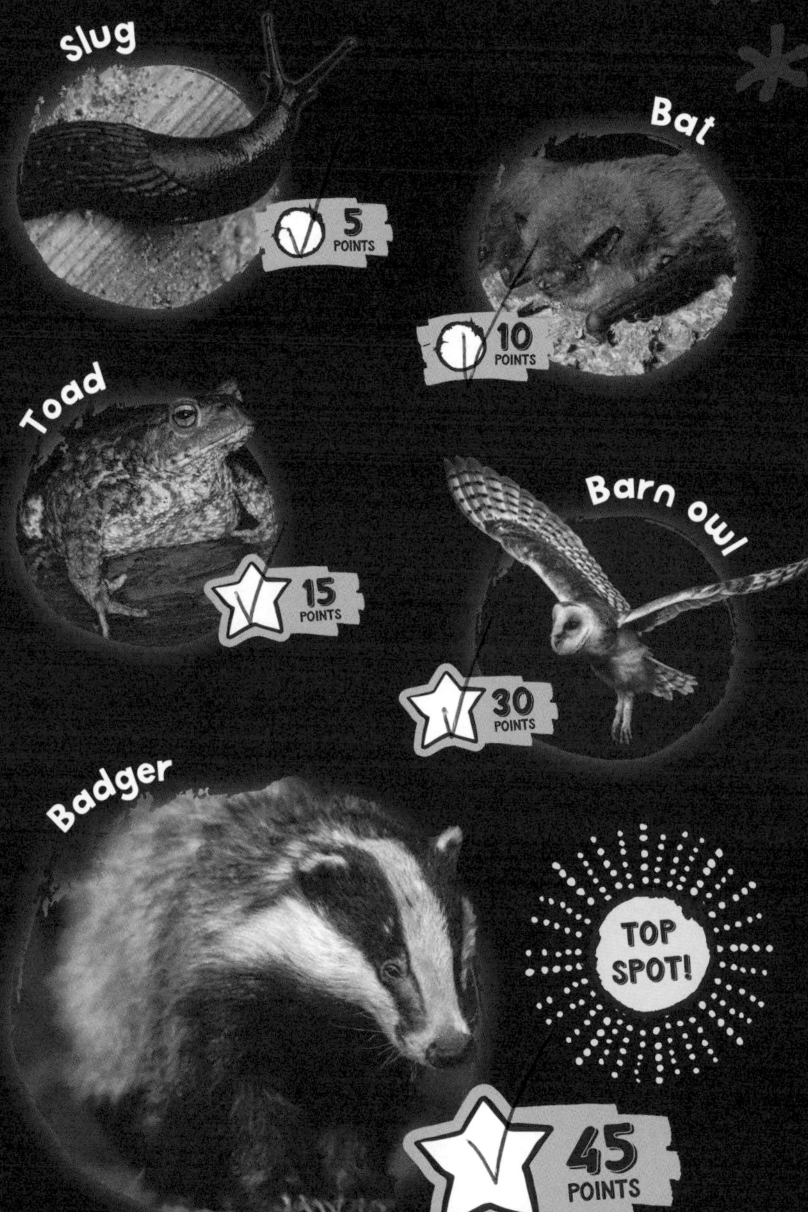

Be an animal detective

People who study animals use signs such as dens, pawprints, leftover meals, territory markings, fur and droppings to help them get an idea of the kind and number of animals in an area and their behaviour.

What to do:

1. Find some animal poo and take a note of its size, shape and colour. You can always break it apart using a stick to see what's inside. Never touch poo with your hands as it may contain harmful bacteria.

Rabbit/hare poo is usually found in a cluster of small, round balls. It is usually a green-brown colour from their diet of mostly grass.

Fox poo is usually quite smelly and dog-like. It may contain fur or feathers from its last meal.

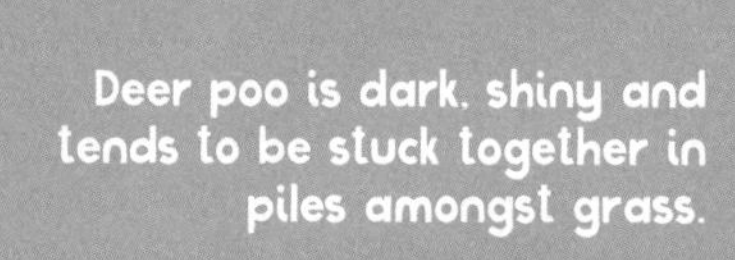

Deer poo is dark, shiny and tends to be stuck together in piles amongst grass.

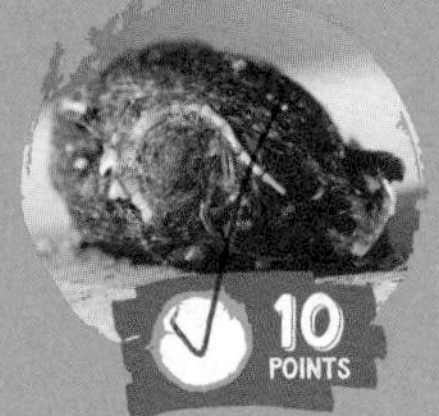

Owl pellets are in fact not poo, but regurgitated undigested food such as bones or fur coughed up through the beak. Barn owl pellets turn from black to grey as they dry out.

2 Another way to track animals is by looking out for their pawprints. They are often left behind in soft mud or sand. See if you can spot any animal tracks when you're out on a nature walk.

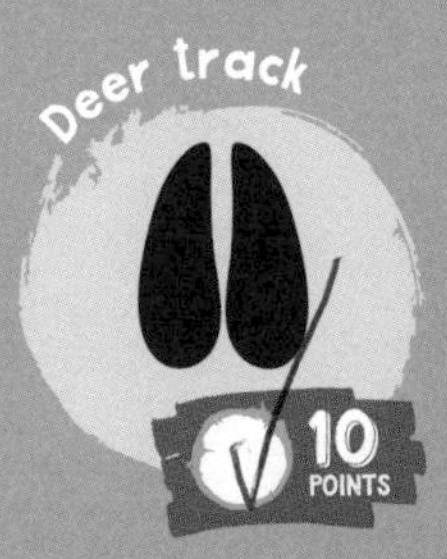

Score 30 eco points if you record your findings with a mammal survey, such as those at **mammal.org.uk** – these help save threatened species.

Build a bird feeder

What to do:

1. Wash out the bottle and remove the cap. Make a few small holes in the bottom of the bottle with a pin, for drainage.
2. Carefully use scissors to make two level holes on opposite sides of the bottle near the bottom.
3. Slide a stick through these holes. You need around 5 cm of stick outside the bottle on each side to form perches.
4. Cut feeding holes in the bottle above the perches.
5. Cut holes near the neck of the bottle for the string.
6. Fill your bottle with seed mix (this is easiest with a funnel) and screw on the cap.
7. Hang your feeder from a branch.

You'll need:

old plastic bottle (with cap), stick, pin, scissors, string, bird seed mix, funnel

Score 10 eco points for keeping your feeder topped up with seed, especially during the winter.

Here are some colourful vistors you might get to your bird feeder – tick them off as you spot them, and don't forget to take some snaps!

Bluetit

A colourful and popular garden visitor, bluetits are attracted to most bird feeders.

5 POINTS

Siskin

The male siskin has a black head and more yellow colours on its underside.

10 POINTS

Goldfinch

Red faced and with golden wings, this little finch is easy to recognise.

15 POINTS

Bullfinch

The male bullfinch has a bright pinkish-red breast, while the female's is orange-brown in colour.

TOP SPOT!

45 POINTS

Make a compost bin

Wildlife loves a compost heap! A large pile of rotting vegetation generates heat which makes it a wonderful home for hedgehogs, slow worms and grass snakes. Making your own compost is better for the environment as it recycles items that would normally be thrown out.

You'll need:

a quiet, shaded corner outside, plastic bin or wooden box, drill, shredded newspaper or straw, soil

What to do:

1. Ask an adult to drill eight holes in the bottom of your plastic container and four holes up each side. This will allow air to circulate around your recycled compost bin.
2. Fill the bottom of the container with a thick layer of newspaper or straw and then add lots of soil on top.
3. Fill your compost bin with rotting fruit, teabags, potato peels, eggshells, grass clippings and dead leaves.
4. When it is full keep the lid on and wait three months. Then you will have nutrient-rich soil to use.

Don't put animal waste, meat, dairy or bones into your compost bin as it will lead to harmful bacteria growing and give off a nasty smell!

Score 20 eco points for turning all your banana peels and other waste into high quality compost!

20 ECO POINTS

Make seed bombs

Throwing seed bombs into your garden or a wild patch of grass is an excellent way to grow flowers and help insect species by providing them with a source of food.

You'll need:

bowl, meadow flower seeds, compost, powdered clay (usually found in craft shops)

What to do:

1. Mix into your bowl one cup of seeds with five cups of compost and two cups of powdered clay.
2. Add little bits of water at a time and mix with your hands until it all begins to stick together.
3. Once the mixture is firm and sticky, roll it into balls.
4. Leave the balls to dry outside somewhere sunny and warm.
5. When they are dry you can 'bomb' away! Throw your balls at bare patches of soil or grass. Over the next few weeks watch what flowers grow from those spots.

Score 30 eco points if you use your own compost (see opposite page)!

30 ECO POINTS

19

Attract creepy crawlies

Many insects and creepy crawlies, including butterflies and bees, love flowers, so planting lots of native species of flower provides them with food and shelter. But did you know there are many other ways to help other bug species too?

Make a log pile

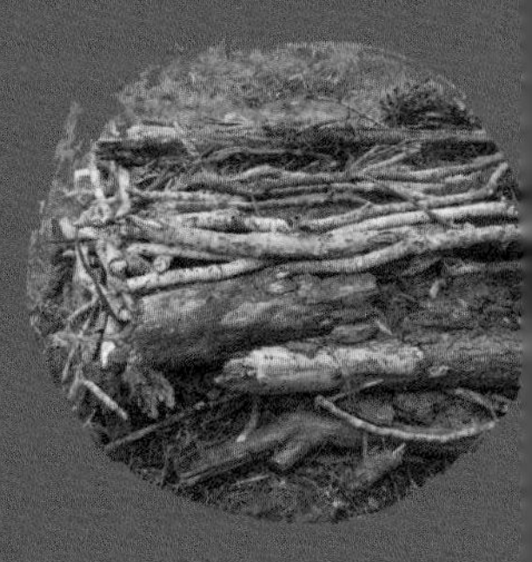

Lots of minibeasts and even amphibians love to hibernate through the winter underneath logs. In a quiet spot make a pile of logs and twigs (even one large log will provide hundreds of different insects with shelter). In the autumn, when leaves start to drop off the trees, cover your log pile with fallen leaves to provide a food source. When you are happy with your pile try not to disturb it too much.

Enjoy the mess

Everyone enjoys a tidy garden, but did you know insects thrive amongst long, messy grass? If you can, dedicate one little patch to insects and avoid strimming it with a lawnmower or pulling out the weeds. Put up a sign saying, 'Wildlife Garden', so everyone knows you are helping the environment and not being lazy!

Score 20 eco points if you make BOTH of these insect-friendly projects. A real insect hero!

20 ECO POINTS

Once you've started attracting different bugs and creepy crawlies, you might want to identify them. Check out the ones below and see if you can spot any in your log pile or wildlife garden.

20

Save the bees

Bumblebees may become tired after being caught in bad weather or having been stuck on the ground for a long time. If you see a bee unable to fly and in distress, one way of helping them is by giving them an energy boost... by preparing them a sugary snack.

You'll need:

white sugar (not brown as bees find this hard to digest), container, teaspoon, warm water, a piece of paper

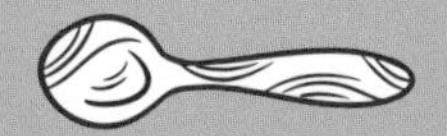

What to do:

1. If it is safe to do so, move the bee to a warm, dry surface outside using a piece of paper.
2. Mix 50:50 white sugar and warm water in a container, until the sugar dissolves.
3. With your teaspoon, spoon out some of the sugar water and offer it gently to the bee.
4. If the bee drinks some of the liquid off the spoon, repeat the process and then stand back and wait for the bee to recover in the sunshine.

Once you've saved any bees in distress, you can make sure that your garden is as bee friendly as possible, which will help keep them happy and safe nearby.

Make a bee-friendly water station

If you have a bird bath or pond, try filling up one side with rocks and stones. Ensure part of the stones stick up through the surface of the water. Bees aren't great swimmers so if they fall into water they risk drowning. Providing bees with a safe area to land, but making sure they can still reach the water to drink, will save lots of 'buzzy-bee' lives.

Score 20 eco points for saving a bee! Bee numbers are dropping all over the world because some of their habitats are being polluted, or even destroyed. Bees have a really important part to play in many ecosystems, and they help pollinate plants, so without them, many plants and other animal species will be at risk of extinction too.

21

Build a 'bee & bee' for bees, wasps and hoverflies

Solitary bees and wasps don't live in hives, but instead make homes in tunnels. You can offer them a cosy place to stay, during spring, by building a 'bee & bee'.

You'll need:

weather-proof box, sticks/twigs, string, nails, different-sized hollow tubes (e.g. garden canes) – all about 15 cm long

What to do:

1. Tightly pack the weather-proof box with the different-sized hollow tubes.
2. Fill any gaps between the tubes with sticks or twigs.
3. Ask a grown-up to help you attach your box to a wall or a fence with string and nails. Make sure it faces south, in an area that gets lots of sun. Position it about waist level.
4. Watch your happy new tenants move in!

Here are some of the buzzy creatures you might find in and around your new 'bee & bee'. Be careful not to touch or get too close – some of them could sting you!

Common wasp

10 POINTS

White-tailed bumblebee

15 POINTS

Honey bee

15 POINTS

Red mason bee

5 POINTS

Hornet mimic hoverfly

TOP SPOT!

25 POINTS

Make duck and swan food

Feeding ducks and swans bread is a very common sight around parks and ponds, but it isn't very nutritious for them at all and can even make them sick.

You'll need:

lettuce such as romaine (not iceberg), porridge oats, sweetcorn, frozen peas (the amounts don't matter), large bowl, container

What to do:

1. Defrost some peas by leaving in the fridge overnight.
2. Drain the sweetcorn, or defrost like the peas if frozen.
3. Into your bowl, add the peas, sweetcorn and porridge oats.
4. Tear your lettuce into small pieces and add that to your bowl too.
5. Mix everything together with your hands (wash them first!).
6. Fill a container with your duck and swan food. It will keep in the fridge for about 5 days.
7. Go to your local pond and throw handfuls of the mixture to the ducks and swans in the water.

Lots of different bird species use ponds to find food and raise their young. Can you spot...?
Coot
5 POINTS
Mallard
5 POINTS
Canada goose
10 POINTS
Mute swan
10 POINTS
Greylag goose
20 POINTS
Moorhen
15 POINTS
Wigeon
25 POINTS
TOP SPOT!

23

Go pond dipping

Pond dipping is a fantastic way to discover life beneath the water. You'll be amazed at how many animals lurk in the depths of your local pond.

You'll need:

net, tray or clear containers, spoon, magnifier, camera or nature diary, towel (to dry off your hands)

What to do:

1. Ask an adult to take you to a safe spot at a local pond. It's good to pond dip on your knees so you don't lose your balance and fall in the water!
2. Wet your net in the water before moving it around in slow circles.
3. Slowly pull the net from the water and have a look at anything you may have caught.
4. Carefully transfer any plants or animals to a container or onto a tray using a spoon. Always provide some water for any animal you find.
5. Use your magnifier to have a closer look at your catch.
6. Record your finds with a camera or in your nature diary.

Score 20 eco points for returning everything back to where you found it in the pond.

20 ECO POINTS

There may be animals or insects flying or moving above the surface of the water as well as swimming underneath. Can you spot any of these?

Go on a spring or summer flower hunt

Some flowers rely on the wind to carry their pollen to produce more of the same species, but the majority rely on insects for pollination. Flowers attract bumblebees, hoverflies and butterflies with their colourful petals and the promise of sweet nectar. When the insects fly to another flower, they transfer pollen and help more flowers grow.

What to do:

1. Hunt high and low for any wild flowers growing nearby, making a note of all their colours and shapes in your nature diary (see page 8).

2. Can you spot the flowers below and opposite?

Cornflower

The cornflower is found in fields and is surprisingly tall.

Spear thistle

Widespread and common throughout the UK, the spear thistle can grow up to a metre and has spiny stems.

Common poppy

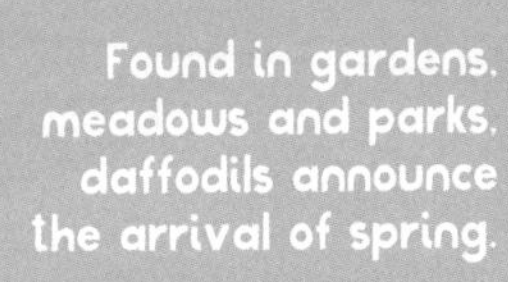

Found in fields and roadside verges, poppies flower from June to August.

Daffodil

Found in gardens, meadows and parks, daffodils announce the arrival of spring.

Bluebell

Bluebells appear in ancient woodlands between April and May. They are protected in the UK so don't pick or trample them.

Make perfume with petals

Anyone can make perfume from their own home! Flower petals create a lovely scent. Recommended petals to use are from roses and honeysuckle.

You'll need:

flower petals, cheesecloth, bowl with lid, small pot, small container

What to do:

1. Collect your petals into a pile.
2. Drape your cheesecloth over the sides of your bowl and place the petals on top.
3. Pour a small amount of water into the bowl to submerge your petals, but make sure the edges of your cheesecloth are still hanging out the rim of the bowl and cover the bowl with a lid.
4. Leave your petals to soak overnight.
5. The next day, lift the cheesecloth and soaked petals out of the bowl and squeeze the flower-scented water into a small pot.
6. With the help of an adult simmer the liquid over a low heat until you have a few teaspoons of water.
7. Allow the liquid to cool and then bottle your perfume.

Write a letter to help protect roadside verges

Roadside verges provide food for insects and are natural corridors, creating a safe passage for animals to move from one habitat to another. They also provide space for many rare meadow wildflowers, which is very important as the UK has lost 97% of its meadows since the 1930s.

What to do:

1. Ask an adult to find out who your local MP is in your area and either send them an email or post a letter to their office.
2. Your letter should be polite and informative.
3. You may want to include how important the management of roadside verges are to wildlife and plant life, and the benefits they bring by helping to reduce global warming.
4. You may want to ask them to reconsider cutting back grass and flowers along roadside verges unnecessarily as many insects depend on them for food.
5. Once you have all your points written down, remember to leave your name and a way for your MP to contact you to let you know what they are doing to help.

Score 10 eco points when you have completed and sent your letter.

10 ECO POINTS

Make a butterfly feeding station

There are plenty of opportunities to see butterflies through summer until early autumn. Making a feeder is a great way to give these insects a helping hand and see them up close.

You'll need:

plastic tub lid, hole punch or scissors, colourful beads, string or wool, soft fruit (the riper the better)

What to do:

1. Punch or cut four holes at equal distances apart around your tub lid.
2. Cut four pieces of wool or string into equal lengths, thread each through a hole in the lid and secure each at the bottom with a large knot.
3. Thread coloured beads on to each piece of string or wool, about halfway up their length, and then tie all four pieces together. The colour of the beads attracts butterflies to your feeder – just like how flowers use their coloured petals to do the same thing.
4. Find a tree branch or fence post (preferably near flowers) to hang your butterfly feeder.
5. Fill the plate with soft fruits. Butterflies love overly ripe banana, orange, strawberry, peach, nectarine and apple!

Butterflies are some of the most common insects in the UK with some 59 species found across Britain. Can you spot some of the most well-known?

Butterflies are an important part of the food chain and very good indicators of change in the environment. Score 20 eco points for building your feeding station.

20 ECO POINTS

Organise a litter pick

Litter can be a real problem for wildlife. Organising a local litter pick is one way you can help keep an area tidy and ensure wildlife stays safe!

You'll need:

bin bags, litter picker, hi-vis vest

What to do:

1. Check if there's a local litter pick group already in your area. If there is, why not join? And if not, start your own!
2. When you have chosen a spot you would like to clear of litter, you need to contact the land owner to get permission. Check with an adult to find out if the area is private or public land.
3. Contact your local council who should provide you with the equipment you need, including bags and litter pickers. They will also tell you a dedicated spot where you can leave your filled bags so they can collect them for you.
4. Ask your friends to help out and make sure there is always an adult with you.
5. Fill your bags with rubbish and when you are finished give yourself a pat on the back for doing a good deed for nature.

Score 20 eco points for encouraging others to join you on your litter pick!

A build-up of litter in urban areas can attract wildlife, but it can often be harmful to the animal if they eat things they shouldn't eat, or if they get trapped or tangled in packaging. These are some animals you could help save by binning your own litter, and going on a litter pick. Can you spot...?

Watch birds...

Birds are all around us. They are an excellent group of animals to learn about as you are guaranteed a chance to see and hear them.

What to do:

1. Watch birds from a distance – never disturb them, their nests or their habitats.
2. Report your sightings on BirdTrack (**bto.org**) and record in your nature diary.

You'll need:

warm clothes, sturdy shoes, binoculars, your nature diary

Score if you see these birds.

...and listen to them

Between March and July, if you wake early enough you will be able to hear birds singing to one another to find a mate or defend their territory. This is called the dawn chorus.

What to do:

1. Pick a dry, clear day with no wind and go outside about an hour before the Sun rises.
2. Close your eyes and listen to the birds singing. How many different calls can you make out?
3. Go to **rspb.org.uk/birds-and-wildlife/bird-songs** to identify the songs you've heard.

These birds are some of the earliest to sing during spring. Score when you hear them!

Build a hedgehog house

A hedgehog house provides a safe space for an animal whose population has drastically fallen across the UK.

You'll need:

untreated timber, jigsaw, hammer, nails, 2 metal hinges, polythene sheet, dry leaves, straw

What to do:

1. Ask an adult to help you build your hedgehog home or look online to buy one ready-made.
2. Start to make the hedgehog house by cutting six 30 cm x 30 cm panels of your untreated timber.
3. Use your hammer and nails to attach the hinges, joining two of the panels – this will create a roof for easy access into the house to clean it when not in use.
4. Cut out a doorway of 15 cm x 15 cm in the middle of one of the other panels.
5. Using more untreated timber, make a tunnel leading into the house by cutting out four 30 cm x 15 cm panels. Nail the panels together to make a rectangular tunnel.

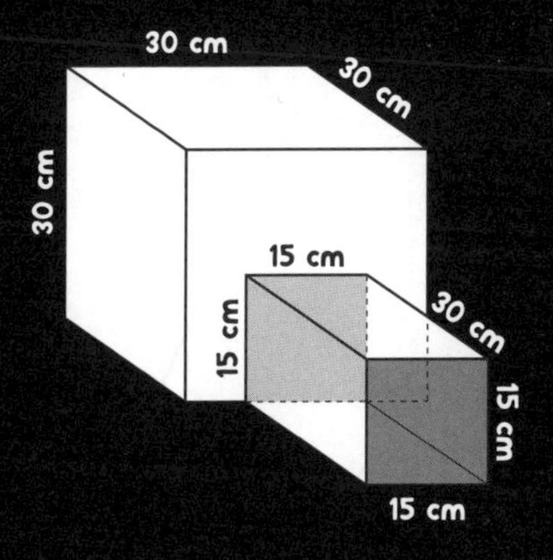

6. Attach your tunnel with nails to the panel with the doorway cut out (be careful there are no nails sticking out of the wood).

7. Create the main chamber of the house by making a box shape with the 30 cm x 30 cm panels and nail them in place.

8. Find a quiet, sheltered area for your hedgehog house and make sure the opening of the tunnel faces south.

9. Fill the house with lots of straw to make a warm bed, and then cover the roof with a sheet of polythene to protect it from the wind and rain.

10. Lastly, cover the polythene sheet with sticks and dry leaves to camouflage the home.

Remember to clean out the hedgehog house once a year between late March and April, when the hedgehog has finished hibernating, to keep it free from parasites and pests!

Score 30 eco points for building your hedgehog house. It will allow a hedgehog to hibernate through the winter safe from predators and the cold.

Make a windowsill garden box

Even if you live in an apartment or don't have access to a back garden, creating a windowsill garden allows you to enjoy the benefits of being outside.

You'll need:

clear storage box, organic potting soil with compost, seeds of your choice or house plants to pot, tray, drill or scissors, figurines to decorate

What to do:

1. Ask an adult to drill or cut small holes in the bottom of the storage box.
2. Place the storage box on a tray that you don't mind getting dirty and fill the box halfway with the soil. The tray will collect water and any loose soil, so it doesn't mark the floor underneath!
3. Bed any plants or scatter your seeds across the top of the soil and cover with a few more handfuls of soil.
4. Place figurines or information signs about the seeds planted around your windowsill garden to decorate.
5. Place your windowsill garden near a window that gets lots of light and keep your soil hydrated.
6. Wait a few weeks for your chosen seeds to flower or watch your plants grow.

As well as house plants, why not grow strawberries in your windowsill garden box or herbs such as mint and basil? Score for growing any of these plants or for any you see growing on anyone else's window ledge.

32

Identify trees by seeds and leaves

Leaves come in a variety of shapes and sizes which you can use to identify which tree they came from.

What to do:

1. Find some trees nearby.
2. If it's autumn or winter, there will likely be leaves or seeds on the ground below a tree – collect these in a bag to take home and identify. See if you can spot these seeds:

3 If it's spring or summer, a tree's leaves and seeds will likely be higher up, and still attached to the tree. Don't pick leaves off trees – you could try photographing them instead. Can you find these green leaves?

Plant a tree

Trees are some of the most important life forms around us – not only do they provide food and shelter to wildlife and us, but they also purify the air we breathe. Planting a tree is a great way to give back to nature.

Autumn is a good time to plant trees as the still-warm soil allows roots to be established before the winter cold.

You'll need:

shovel, wellies, gloves, seeds, plant pot, compost, stones, mesh

What to do:

1. Begin by selecting a place to plant your tree. The area you choose must not have underground cables or overhead obstacles as your tree and roots will grow.
2. Place some stones at the bottom of a plant pot and fill with compost.
3. Place the seeds about 2 cm into the compost and then flatten down and water thoroughly.

4. Place the pot in a quiet, shady spot outdoors and cover the top with mesh to stop animals getting to the seeds.

5. Re-pot the shoot into larger pots as it grows and when the sapling is about half a metre tall transfer it into the ground.

6. Make a hole in the ground about three times the width of your plant pot and just as deep, making sure there is plenty of room for the roots.

7. Remove the sapling from the pot and before placing it into the hole, stick it into a bucket of water so the roots are well hydrated.

8. Once your ball of roots has had a good drink, place it into the newly dug hole.

9. With your shovel, carefully loosen the root ball to encourage the roots to grow into the new soil that surrounds it.

10. Refill the hole around your newly transferred tree and pat the soil firmly with your shovel to secure it.

11. You have planted your very first tree! If you want to plant any more, leave about a 2-metre gap between the saplings.

Score 20 eco points if you plant a native species of tree such as Alder, Elder or Crab Apple. A native species is one that occurs naturally in an area. It is much better at supporting local wildlife than a non-native species, which has been brought in from another part of the world.

34

Shake a tree

Shaking a tree branch or 'tree-beating' is a great way to discover what kind of minibeasts live in the trees. If done correctly this activity will cause no harm to the tree or insects that call it their home.

You'll need:

large white piece of paper, magnifying glass, container

What to do:

1. Find a tree with low-hanging branches and have a friend or family member hold the piece of paper underneath.
2. Gently shake the tree for five seconds and watch bugs and leaves fall on to your paper.
3. Lower the paper to the ground and use a magnifier to have a closer look at what fell.
4. How many species can you identify?
5. Once you are finished inspecting, carefully return everything back to the tree.

Did any of these creepy crawlies fall from the tree when you gave it a shake?

Caterpillar

5 POINTS

Aphid

5 POINTS

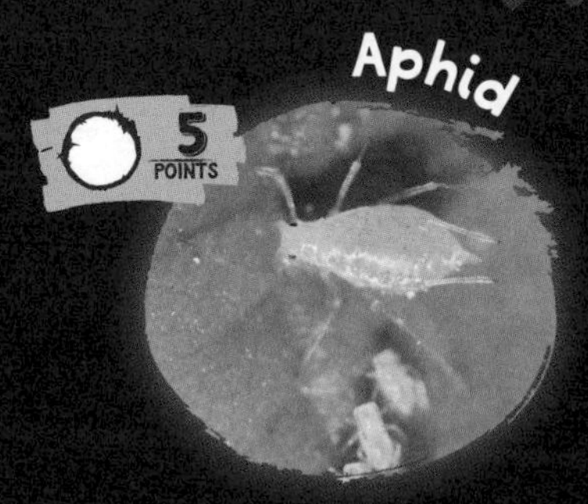

Snail

5 POINTS

Harvestman

10 POINTS

Grasshopper

15 POINTS

Centipede

TOP SPOT!

35 POINTS

Tell the age of a tree

It is difficult to tell the age of most wild animals if you haven't been studying them since birth. However, one group of living things that you can tell the age of is trees! When a tree falls or is cut down you can tell how old it was when it died.

What to do:

1. Look closely at the cross section of the tree trunk and you'll see a series of rings, each inside another, from the centre to the edge.
2. Each ring represents one year of the tree's life and so by counting them all you will be able to work out how many years old the tree was before it died or was chopped down.
3. The distance between the rings can also tell you whether the tree had a good year or not. For instance, if it was a hot, dry summer, the tree might not have been able to grow as much and the gap between the rings will be narrow. A wet summer means the tree stayed hydrated and could grow more so the distance between the two rings will be wider.
4. Count the rings from the centre outwards. The centre rings are the oldest and the ones closest to the bark are the most recent.

Learn how water travels through leaves

Ever wondered how plants drink without a mouth? This fun experiment shows you how water travels through leaves and hydrates the whole of the plant or tree.

You'll need:

leaves, scissors, clear cup, food colouring (red or blue works best)

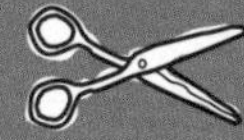

What to do:

1. Collect a few different types of leaves – the larger the better!
2. Trim the bottom of each leaf stem and then fill a glass of water for each chosen leaf, just over half full.
3. Place each leaf, stem facing downwards, into the water, but leave the head of the leaf sticking above the water line.
4. Add a dark colour of food colouring to the water.
5. Over the next three days watch as the leaf changes colour as the coloured water is absorbed up through the stem.

The coloured water moves through the xylem tubes of the leaf. These tubes help plants transport water and essential minerals from the roots, at the bottom, through every leaf and structure of the plant or tree.

Go on a fungi hunt

Fungi (mushrooms and toadstools) are neither plant nor animal, but are in fact their own unique group of living things. They grow everywhere from on trees, amongst grass, in gardens and even on walls. With fungi easy to find on nature walks it's good to learn what some species are called.

Autumn is a great time to spot fungi, so pick a nice sunny autumn day, pack something warm to wear, and your nature diary, and head out to a local woodland or park to see if you can spot any fungi.

Did you spot any of these?

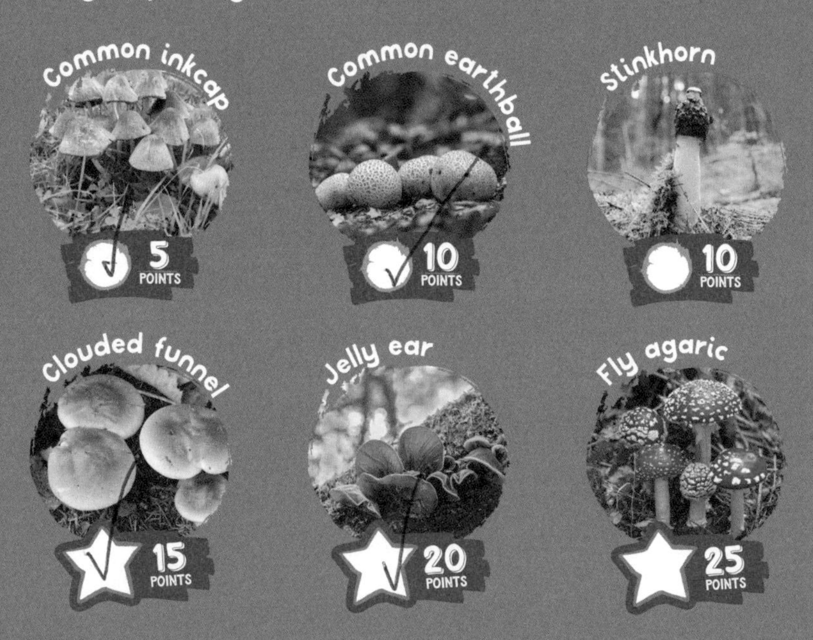

Never touch a fungus without asking a grown-up – some species are poisonous. If you do touch fungi, always remember to wash your hands before touching food or your face.

Forage for berries

Picking berries to eat is a great spring and summer activity whether it is out in the woods or on a farm. Not all berries are safe to eat however, so always ask a grown-up before trying any.

You'll need:

thick gloves, scissors, container to store berries, sturdy shoes

What to do:

1. Look for berries in hedgerows and use your gloves and scissors to gently pick them.
2. When your container is full of juicy berries, take them home to wash and eat or even cook with.

Can you spot any of these berries which are safe to eat?

Score 10 eco points for making your own jam or dessert from the berries you collect. This is better for the environment as fuel is being saved by not transporting the berries!

10 ECO POINTS

Go on a deer watch

There are six species of deer living across the UK. Many parks, farmland and woods in the UK are home to large populations of wild deer so find one near you, and ask a grown-up to take you. You'll need to be quiet if you're trying to spot a deer as they can be easily frightened.

What to do:

Find a deer and follow the flowchart below to work out which one you have seen...

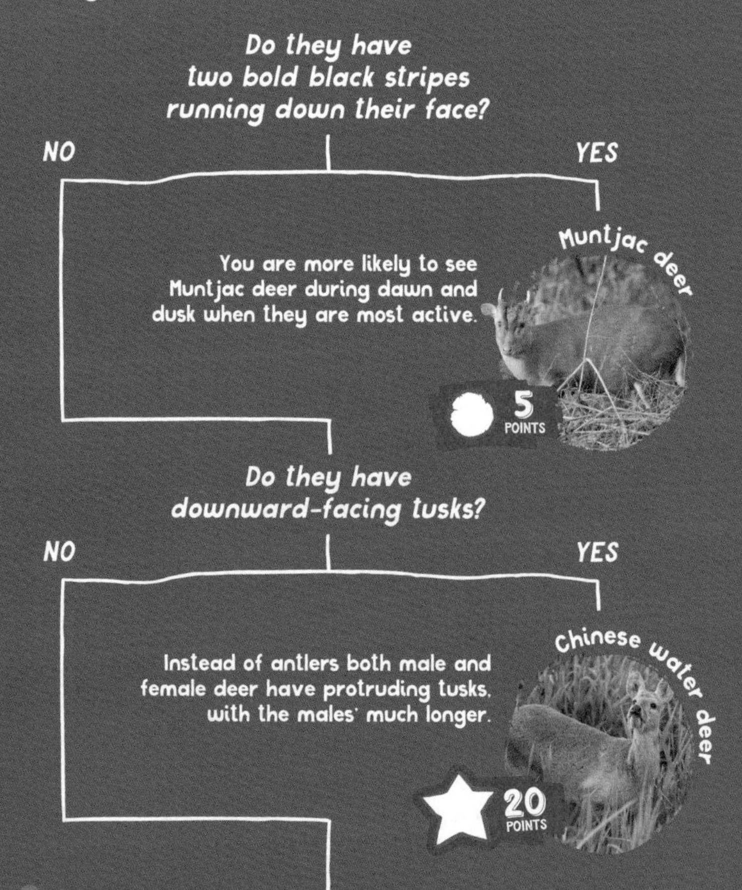

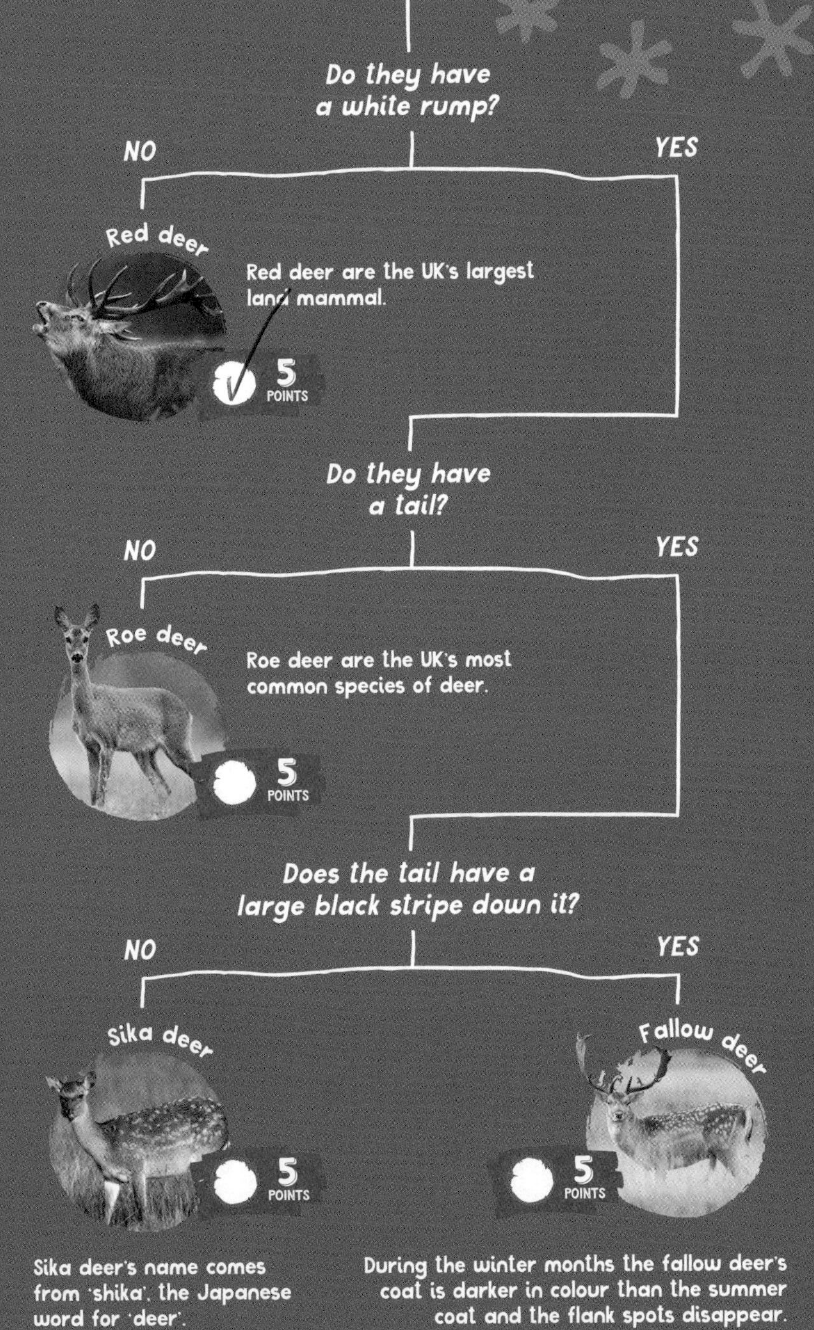

Sika deer's name comes from 'shika', the Japanese word for 'deer'.

During the winter months the fallow deer's coat is darker in colour than the summer coat and the flank spots disappear.

Explore a river

Rivers are great places to explore and get outside with nature, but they can also be dangerous so make sure an adult knows where you are.

You'll need:

wellies, change of clothing, towel, hand sanitiser

Explore safely:

Safe areas of the river to stick to:

1. A gravel beach section – this will allow you to get near the water safely.
2. Shallow riverbanks – the gentle slope will allow you to get in and out the river easily.
3. Clear water – you should be able to see your feet clearly through the water. Brown water may mean there has been recent rainfall and the river is not suitable to be in.

Areas to avoid:

1. Steep riverbanks – risk of slipping and falling into the water.
2. Deep or fast-flowing water – always stay in shallow areas.

Always check the weather forecast before heading out and be prepared for your visit!

Lots of animals like to spend their time around a water source. Have you spotted any of these near or in a river?

Build a dam

Beavers are excellent builders, known for constructing dams from gnawed trees. They don't actually live in the dams, but instead build them to keep the family group safe from predators. The dam creates a pond of deep water, which predators can't access, and where these rodents build their real home – a small lodge that keeps them dry and safe and able to store food. Can you build a dam as efficiently as a beaver?

You'll need:

large plastic container, sand, stones, lollipop sticks, bucket of water

What to do:

1. Fill your container half full of sand and scoop a path through the middle for your river to run through.
2. Build a dam across the path that the water will run down using lollipop sticks and stones.
3. Slowly pour water from your bucket in one side of the container and wait until it reaches your dam – did any water make it through?
4. Keep adding to your dam until the water is completely blocked on one side!

Can you spot signs of beaver activity?

Gnawed tree

Beavers first start building by gathering wood to create the dam, which they collect by gnawing away at the bark of trees near to a river.

Beaver dam

15 POINTS

Beaver dams are usually around 1.5 metres high and are held together by branches, leaves, stones and uprooted plants.

Beaver lodge

When the water levels begin to rise in their dammed area, the beavers start to build their lodge.

Beaver

30 POINTS

TOP SPOT!

These animals are extremely clever and excellent builders – no wonder they have the nickname 'nature's engineers'!

Make an underwater scope

With an underwater viewer you can see up close how life thrives without disturbing any animals or plants. You can use your scope to further explore rivers, lakes and ponds.

You'll need:

clear plastic bottle, clear plastic wrap, large elastic bands, scissors, bucket

What to do:

1. With the help of a grown-up, use scissors to cut off both ends of the plastic bottle and discard.
2. Cover one end with clear plastic wrap and secure tightly with elastic bands.
3. Test your scope by sticking the plastic wrap end into a full bucket of water to make sure it is leak proof.
4. Get exploring! Find a pond or river to test out your underwater scope. Look through it into the water to see what you can see below the surface.

Score 10 eco points for using a recycled plastic bottle.

Who knows what you might see under water! Here are a few creatures you might be lucky enough to find...

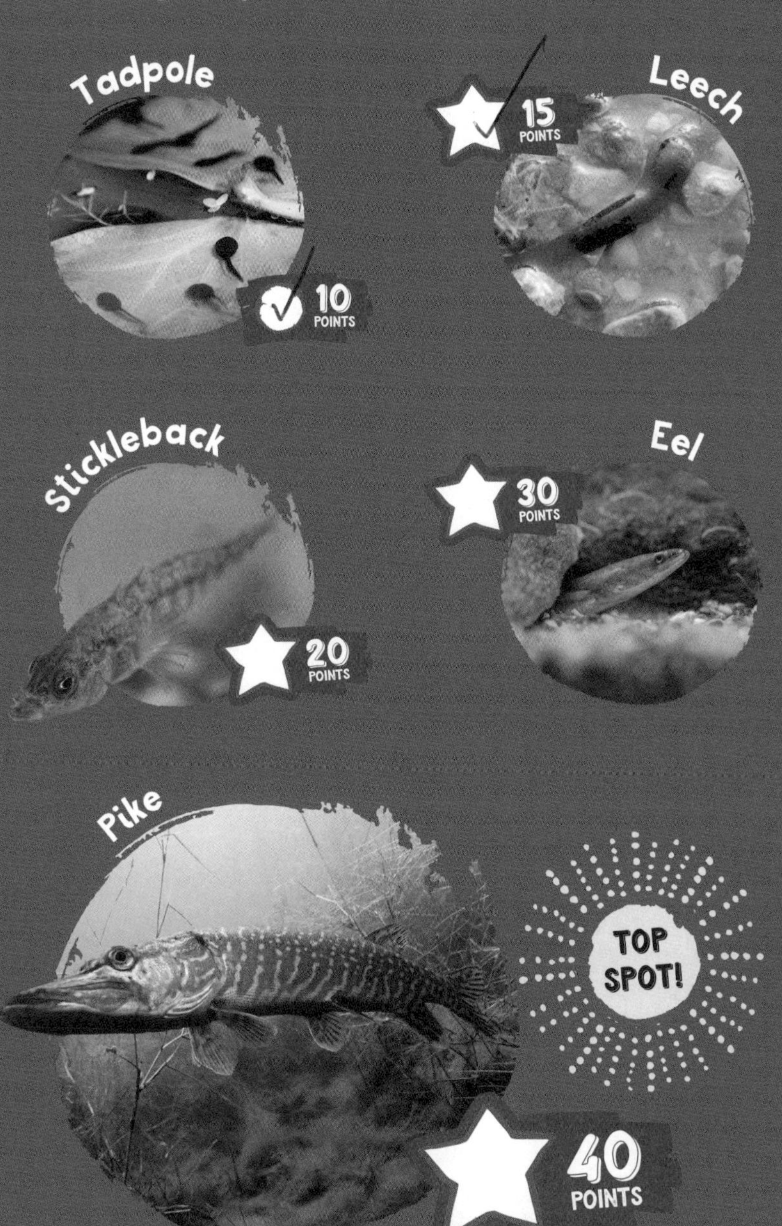

Have a stick race

Fans of Winnie the Pooh may know this game as Poohsticks – a fun game to play outside with friends. The World Poohsticks Championship is held in Little Wittenham, Oxfordshire, in late March each year.

You'll need:

sticks about 30 cm long, notepad and pen, whistle

What to do:

1. Gather a group of friends and each collect three to five sticks – make sure you can tell the difference between them.
2. Find a bridge nearby where water runs underneath.
3. Everyone line up on one side and when the whistle goes, drop one stick each into the water below.
4. Then run to the other side of the bridge and watch whose stick emerges from the other side first.
5. They are the winner of that round. Use your notepad and pen to keep score.
6. The game ends when everyone has used up their sticks and the victor is the person who has won the most stick races.

Hug a tree

Hug a tree. No, really! Science has shown that by hugging a tree your body releases a hormone that helps keep you calm and happy. The same hormone is released when you pet a cat or dog.

Keeping a healthy body and mind is so important for our wellbeing and one way to do that is by spending time in the natural world. Everything is connected – fungi, plants and animals – and we rely on one another to survive.

Spending time outside in the fresh air does wonders for us all, so next time you come across a tree, don't be shy! Give it a good, old cuddle.

What to do:

When you're hugging your chosen tree, think about the following things...

1. How did you feel before going on a walk outside amongst the trees?
2. How did you feel after hugging a tree and spending time in nature?
3. Did you notice anything different? Did you feel happier and calmer for being outside?

45

Mindfulness moment

Science shows that diving underwater, swimming in water, sitting near water and even listening to water can help us become calm and relaxed.

Sometimes life can be busy and maybe a little stressful; sometimes we feel angry or sad. One way to help boost your mood is to find your favourite spot beside a lake or pond and practise mindfulness.

What is mindfulness?

Mindfulness is taking a moment of your day to sit, close your eyes and just think about your breathing. Breathing in and out. In and out. Try and clear your mind of everything but your breath and be completely in the present moment.

Sometimes it can be hard to not think about anything, so start off doing so for 10 seconds, then 30 seconds and then a full minute.

Taking a moment for yourself each day to be mindful can improve your mood, help your focus and boost your energy levels.

You don't need to be near water to be mindful. Nature in general can help you have mindful moments. Next time you're out and about, try and focus all five of your senses on calming things...

Soothing sounds

What can you hear?

Beautiful scenery

What can you see?

Fragrant flowers

What can you smell?

Smooth textures

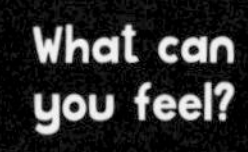

What can you feel?

Salty sea air

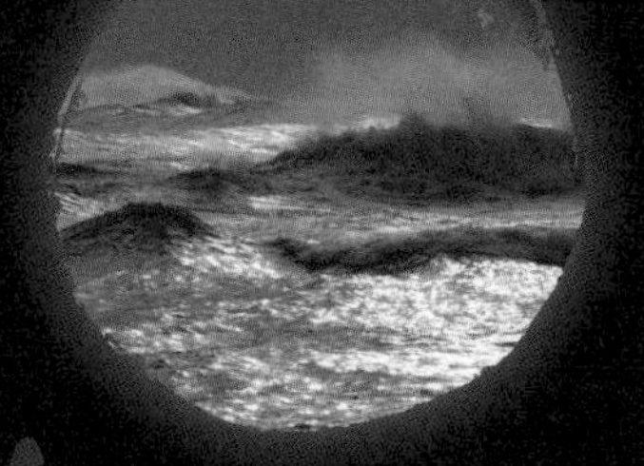

What can you taste?

Build a sandcastle

Ever dreamed of being a king or a queen? Building a castle out of sand is a good start! You just need to visit a sandy beach first. The best time to build a sandcastle is just as the tide is going out and the sand is still damp.

You'll need:

bucket, spade, flags, shells, pebbles

What to do:

1. Start by drawing a circle in the sand – this will be the moat around your castle.
2. Once the circle is complete begin to dig out the sand, digging about 20 cm deep, following your line in the sand.
3. To make the turrets, fill your bucket up with sand. Make sure the sand is packed tightly at the bottom and lies smooth at the top.
4. Flip your bucket over and hit the top of it with your spade to release all the sand.
5. Carefully lift your bucket away.
6. Once you have your turrets, decorate them with flags, shells and pebbles.
7. Use your now empty bucket to fill your moat with water.

Here are some types of shell you might find at the beach that could come in handy for decorating your sandcastle. Can you spot any?

Go rockpooling

Rock pools are filled with seawater during high tide and when the tide retreats pools of water full of marine life are left behind. It is best to explore rock pools towards the end of spring and on a day when the weather is calm, so you can see clearly and stay safe. The rock pools closest to the water will host all types of life including fish, crabs and barnacles.

Always make sure you check tide times for the beach you are visiting – you don't want to get trapped!

You'll need:

wellies, net, bucket, camera, nature diary, pen or pencil

What to do:

1. With the help of a grown-up, pick a safe spot to explore rock pools.
2. Fill your bucket with water from one of the pools and wet your net.
3. Carefully explore the pool, moving the sand at the bottom gently with your net (the sand at the bottom is a good place to find small shrimp and fish).
4. Once you have caught something in your net place it in your bucket for a closer look.
5. Record all the animals and plants you see with a camera or in your nature diary.

Animals and plants found in rock pools are extremely resilient, surviving a constantly changing environment, including temperatures, oxygen levels, sunlight and disturbance.

Always remember to only put one animal at a time into your bucket when exploring rock pools and to return everything to where you found it. Can you spot...?

Common limpet

These molluscs can attach firmly to rocks and can be found in areas of high wave exposure.

5 POINTS

Common mussel

These fast-growing organisms live in tightly clustered colonies on rocks, usually in sheltered spaces.

5 POINTS

Shore crab

Their shells can be up to 8 cm in diameter, with five serrated 'teeth' on each side.

20 POINTS

Common starfish

Starfish mouths are found on the underside of their body and connected almost directly to their stomach.

25 POINTS

TOP SPOT!

Beadlet anemone

Their tentacles are red, brown or green and can grow up to 7 cm. They can also survive for a time out of the water.

35 POINTS

48

Make a mini beach

Recycling glass, paper and plastic reduces demand for raw materials and helps to conserve natural resources like trees and peat. One item you may find around your household that is easy to recycle are glass jars!

Make a mini beach inside a glass jar to remember your fun day out and always have the ocean near you!

You'll need:

glass jar, paint brush, acrylic paint or stickers, sand, shells and other items found at the beach

What to do:

1. Decorate your glass jar with paint or stickers and take it to the beach with you.
2. Fill the bottom half of your jar with sand.
3. On top of the sand decorate with shells, dried seaweed, pebbles etc, and even make a sign out of card with a favourite message or quote to stick in the sand!
4. Put the lid of the jar back on tightly to stop any spillage.
5. Enjoy always having a little part of the beach close to you.

Not only can you use jars to create lovely keepsakes, but you can recycle them into vases or candle holders!

Of course you can fill your jar with shells, but you might find other items at the seaside to put in your mini beach. Can you find...?

Go seal watching

There are more than thirty species of seal found around the world, but only two can be seen in the UK – the harbour seal (or 'common seal') and the grey seal.

Spotting a seal colony is a fantastic wildlife experience, but it is very important to follow guidelines to avoid disturbing the seals, as getting too close can cause serious distress and harm to the animals.

What to do:

1. Keep a look out near harbours or rocky coastline for seals.
2. If you're lucky enough to spot one (or more!), follow these golden rules to keep you and the seal(s) safe:
    - Always stay at least 20 metres away from it.
    - Move slowly and stay quiet and calm.
    - Never get in the way of a seal and her pup.
    - Never get between a seal and the safety of the sea.
    - Never take dogs near a seal colony.

Follow this advice and you will not only have a memorable experience, but will have done the right thing by seals too!

These are the two seals that can be spotted around UK coastlines. Keep your eyes peeled for them basking on rocks or popping their heads out of the water in harbours.

There are a few things that can help you tell these seals apart:

- Harbour seals have more rounded faces than grey seals.
- When they get out of the water onto rocks, harbour seals space themselves out, but grey seals clump together more tightly.
- Harbour seals have V-shaped nostrils. Grey seals' nostrils are more like lines.

50

Ditch plastic

Plastic is in almost everything we use from chairs to clothes, electronics, toys and everyday household items. It's even in bank notes! We rely on plastic a lot. The things we love about plastic – it's durability and long-lasting life – are also the causes of environmental damage. A typical toothbrush takes over 300 years to decay when sent to landfill! Unless plastic is recycled or we reduce our use of it, it will remain clogging up landfills and polluting our oceans.

What to do:

Think about these ideas to reduce plastic:

- Use re-useable bottles instead of plastic ones.
- Swap plastic straws for paper or metal ones.
- Replace your plastic toothbrush with one made of bamboo.
- Buy fruit and vegetables without packaging.
- Use shampoo bars instead of buying bottles.
- Buy clothes made from natural or recycled materials.

And now think of your own ways to reduce using plastic! Jot your ideas down and try to start doing them in your daily life.

Score 40 eco points if you do three or more of the ideas above to reduce plastic and help protect the environment.

Have you spotted or used any of these eco-friendly alternatives to plastic yet?

Paper or metal straw

Reusable drinks bottle

Recyclable packaging

Bamboo toothbrush

Shampoo bars

Clothing made from recycled materials

Index

Take on the i-SPY seaside challenge!

Discover more fun and fascinating i-SPY books at collins.co.uk/i-SPY